# 3
# Gymnopédies

*Erik Satie*

*Kevin Mayhew*

We hope you enjoy *Trois Gymnopédies*.
Further copies are available from your local music shop.

In case of difficulty, please contact the publisher direct:

The Sales Department
KEVIN MAYHEW LTD
Rattlesden
Bury St Edmunds
Suffolk IP30 0SZ

Phone 01449 737978
Fax 01449 737834

Please ask for our complete catalogue of outstanding Instrumental Music.

Front Cover: *The South Ledges, Appledore, New Hampshire*
by Childe Hassam (1859-1935).
National Museum of American Art, Smithsonian Institute,
Washington DC / Art Resource / Bridgeman Art Library, London.
Reproduced by kind permission.

Cover designed by Juliette Clarke and Graham Johnstone.
Picture Research: Jane Rayson

First published in Great Britain in 1992 by Kevin Mayhew Ltd.

© Copyright 1992 Kevin Mayhew Ltd.

ISBN 0 86209 348 1
Catalogue No: 3611082

Music Editor: Anthea Smith

Printed and bound in Great Britain

# Contents

# GYMNOPÉDIE I

Erik Satie (1866-1925)

# GYMNOPÉDIE II

### Erik Satie

# GYMNOPÉDIE III

Erik Satie